The Path
to Heaven

Enjoyable Stories about
Learning the Qur'an

The Light, Inc.
26 Worlds Fair Dr. Suite C
Somerset, New Jersey, 08873, USA
www.thelightpublishing.com

Title	The Path to Heaven
Authors	Saim Ari
Editor	Jane Louise Kandur
Art Director	Engin Ciftci
Published by	The Light, Inc.
Printed by	Caglayan A.S. - Izmir, 2006
ISBN	1-932099-30-1

Printed in Turkey

CONTENTS

1- The Right Decision 5

2- The Path to Heaven 9

3- The Greatest Treasure 14

4- A Beautiful Summer 18

5- The Qur'an is a Cure For
   Every Trouble 23

6- A Letter From a Friend 28

7- The Picnic 34

8- The Boy Who Searched For
   Happiness 38

9- The Bright World Under The
   Earth 42

10- Sweet Grandpa 46

THE RIGHT DECISION

They had a good time and the children did not want the lessons to finish. It seemed that they would learn to read the Qur'an quickly.

Jafar had been looking forward to the end of the school year. In spring, he had felt that the blossoming trees and singing birds were celebrating the coming holiday. Now it was summer. But despite all his expectations, he was terribly bored. Soon after the beginning of the holiday, nearly all the children in the neighborhood had gone to the mosque to learn how to read the Qur'an. But Jafar did not want to join his friends, although his parents had asked him to. Jafar had always been a lazy student.

"All work and no play make Jafar a dull boy!" he used to say. He did not believe that learning anything could be enjoyable. However, he was not quite right in this. At the mosque it was not only work, there was also play. Uncle

Bilal, the imam of the mosque, taught his pupils the Qur'an by playing games. Jafar's friends, who went to the lessons were enjoying themselves.

During the first week, Uncle Bilal told them to use the Arabic letters to make a picture. The children drew different shapes on the paper with crayons. Some made a pair of glasses, others drew plates of fruit, or buses... The most interesting picture of the day was hung on the wall where people passing by could see it. After a few days, all the children had learned the letters by heart. In the second week they played a syllable game. The teacher wrote some syllables on small pieces of paper and put them in a jar. Then everybody picked one out and read it. Whoever read the most syllables correctly was the winner of the day. Uncle Bilal would give a small present to the winner. These games were really fun. During the break, he asked riddles and told stories and jokes. They had a good time and the children did not want the lessons to finish. It seemed that they would learn to read the Qur'an quickly. By the third week, some of them were able to read words.

Jafar was bored sitting at home all day, doing nothing. He watched the street from the window of his room. His mother came into his room. Seeing that her son was bored she asked:

"Are you OK, darling?"

"I'm so bored, Mom!"

"Go outside and play with your friends dear."

Jafar complained:

"There's nobody outside. Everybody's at the course."

While she was leaving the room, his mother said:

"But you know that you can go to that course too."

Jafar had already thought of that, but his friends had already learned how to read the Qur'an.

"It's too late, I don't even know anything about the letters," he thought miserably.

The Path to Heaven

Jafar stood up grumpily. He muttered, "I'm going for a walk."

He put on his shoes and went out. There were no children outside, except for a few little girls. He began to walk slowly. He began walking toward the mosque.

"What're they doing inside?" he wondered.

He peeped into the mosque from the window. All the children were sitting in their places, listening to their teacher. Uncle Bilal must be teaching them a new game. All of them were listening carefully. Just then, Uncle Bilal realized that Jafar was looking in from the window. He said to the children that he had to go outside for a minute and that they should continue their lesson. Jafar saw that the teacher had noticed him and he tried to leave.

"Jafar, Jafar, wait!" called Uncle Bilal to him.

"Oh, Uncle Bilal," replied Jafar in surprise.

Uncle Bilal spoke, gently smiling:

"I'm so happy to see you. I need a volunteer for today's game. Would you like to join us?"

Jafar thought for a moment. Well, he didn't have anything better to do.

"I guess," he said. "What am I supposed to do?"

Uncle Bilal explained:

"One of the students will go out of the room. We will write a word on a balloon and hide the balloon. Then we will call him inside. He will try to find where we hid the balloon. As he gets closer to the balloon, we will buzz like a bee. Is it clear?"

It sounded like a fun game.

"Yeah, I see."

"Then I will let you be the first student to go out. Now, wait here."

A bit later he called to Jafar:

"You can come in now."

Jafar, excited, went in. Then the game began. Jafar was pleased to be with his friends again. A few minutes before he had been feeling bored, but now he was cheerful and having a great time. He found the balloon in no time. When he showed it to his friends they all read the word that was on it. Jafar felt a bit envious of his friends. After the lesson, Uncle Bilal came up to Jafar.

"Jafar, all your friends are here, why don't you come too?"

Jafar, embarrassed, answered:

"I would love to, but I guess I'm too late. I don't know anything."

Uncle Bilal said tenderly:

"You don't have to worry, I can help you in the evenings. You're a smart boy. I'm sure you will catch up with your friends very quickly. You might even end up reading better than they do. What do you think?"

"Well, I don't know, do you think I can?"

"Of course you can! Allah says *'And certainly We have made the Qur'an easy to remember, but is there anyone who will mind?'* (54:17). And our Prophet says that *'Whoever reads the Qur'an, learns its verses by heart and takes what Allah has allowed as 'halal' (lawful) and what Allah has forbidden as 'haram' (unlawful), then Allah will put that person in heaven'* (Tirmidhi, Sawab al-Qur'an, 13). Now, don't you want to read the book that will take you to Heaven?"

Jafar's face lit up.

"Yeah, sure Uncle Bilal," he said. "I'll come to the course too."

After that day, Jafar began to learn the Qur'an with his friends. He quickly caught up with the other children. He was very glad that he had made the right decision.

THE PATH TO HEAVEN

"If you live by the Qur'an and are good Muslims, you will be given everything you want in Heaven. However, there is one thing more important; that is, you will have pleased Allah."

Every evening Umar, Asma, and their family would gather to read the Qur'an. They especially liked to read the suras of Yasin, Mulk and Jum'a. After reading, their parents would tell them beautiful stories and teach them about Islam. One night, the whole family made their ablutions and then they went to the living-room. First their mother, and then their father, in their beautiful voices, read the

Qur'an aloud. After they finished, the whole family opened their hands to pray. They prayed for pleasant things from Allah, Who is generous in the blessings He sends to His servants. The children's father then respectfully put the Qur'an in its cover and put it back in its place in the library. Meanwhile, their mother had brought them tea and a freshly baked cake, which smelled delicious. The whole family began to drink tea happily. Umar turned to his father and asked:

"Daddy, is it true that angels come to where the Qur'an is read?"

"Yes, that's right, son."

"Oooh daddy, we just read the Qur'an, so the angels must have come to our house too."

His father smiled at him lovingly. Then his mother added:

"Do you know, I've just remembered a story about Usayd, one of the companions of Prophet Muhammad (pbuh)?"

His father went on:

"Yes, Usayd had a beautiful voice and he was one of the people who could read the Qur'an beautifully. He was the first Muslim from Madina as well."

Their mother took her glass of tea from the tray.

"If you want I can tell you his story."

"Oh, yes, please Mom!"

The children were all ears. Their mother took a sip from her tea and began to tell:

"One night, Usayd was reading the sura al-Baqara from the Qur'an. His horse was tied up close by. All of a sudden the horse reared up. Then Usayd stopped reading. The horse stopped rearing and calmed down. A few moments later, when he began to read again, the horse also began to rear. When Usayd stopped reading, the horse stopped too. Then he again began to read and the horse began rearing again. His son Yahya was standing close to the horse. He glanced up at the sky, and do you know what he saw?"

Umar and Asma said in excitement:

"Tell us, Mommy, what did he see?"

"Something that looked like a cloud was hovering in the sky, and in it there were things that looked like candles."

"Ohhhh! What happened next?"

"In the morning Usayd told Prophet Muhammad (pbuh) about the things he had seen the night before. The Prophet (pbuh) asked him:

"Do you know what they were?"

When Usayd said that he did not know, the Prophet (pbuh) explained:

"They were angels. They came when you spoke. If you had continued reading, they would not have been hidden from everyone, rather everyone would have been able to see them in the morning" (Bukhari, Fada'il al-Qur'an, 15).

Umar's eyes opened in amazement when he heard this. He asked:

"What are angels like?"

His father said:

"They are the creatures - servants - sent in order to help us by Allah Who loves us very much. They are loving and beautiful creatures. They always care about us and they want us to go to Heaven."

Asma asked eagerly:

"Daddy, how do we get to Heaven?"

"We get to Heaven by pleasing Allah."

Umar asked:

"Daddy, can we do good by reading the Qur'an?"

"Yes, dear. It is stated in a hadith: *'Learn the Qur'an. Ten sawabs (rewards) will be given for every letter read in the Qur'an'* (Tirmidhi, Fada'il al-Qur'an, 16).

His mother said:

"Of course, it is not enough to only read the Qur'an. We should live our lives like that of Prophet Muhammad (pbuh) and like it says in the Qur'an, my darling."

Asma was a bit confused.

"Mommy, if we do lots of good things and go to Heaven, what will we find there?"

"Everything. For example, what does my little darling want?"

Asma opened her arms as wide as she could, closed her eyes and said:

"I want a huge house made of candy and chocolate."

Asma hesitated. Maybe she had asked for something that was impossible. She looked at her father's face anxiously:

"Did I ask for too much from Allah, Daddy?"

"No, my darling, nothing is difficult for Allah. He creates everything. You can ask for more."

Asma clapped her hands happily.

"Then I want thousands of baby dolls, rabbits, and lambs, but all of the lambs should be as white as snow."

Her father laughed:

"Why not?"

Umar hearing this, became excited and blurted out:

"I want a bicycle with golden wheels and a ship whose sails are full of stars."

Their parents were pleased by what their children were saying. They hugged them affectionately. Their mother said:

"If you live by the Qur'an and are good Muslims, you will be given everything you want in Heaven. However, there is one thing more important; that is, you will have pleased Allah."

Hearing this pleased the children. Umar said:

"Daddy, I want to learn how to read the Qur'an as quickly as possible. Then I will make Allah happy and I will get to Heaven. I already know the names of the letters. Can we start tomorrow?"

Asma was hopping up and down excitedly. She said:

"Me too! Me too!"

Their father, pleased, answered:

"OK, kids. Starting from tomorrow, I will teach you how to read the Qur'an. I think that you will be able to learn very quickly."

Just then their mother glanced up at the clock on the wall and told them:

"Come on kids, it's long past your bedtime."

"Good night Mommy, good night Daddy!"

As the children were heading to their beds they continued to make a list of their wishes:

"When I go to Heaven, I want a horse with white wings."

"I will ask for thousands of colored balloons and marbles."

"Will you let me play with them too?"

"Well, alright, but only if you let me ride your horse."

"OK! It's a deal."

THE GREATEST TREASURE

"Is it treasure, with gold, silver...?"
"More than that my children, there are not only a few things. There are pearls, rubies, diamonds, more than you can imagine."

"hhhh, grandma! You didn't study!"

"Well, darling, I'm sorry, but you know I was busy yesterday, I had company. Otherwise I would have studied."

"That isn't a good excuse, you should always find some time to repeat the alphabet."

"OK, Insha Allah (if Allah wills), I promise that I will memorize it. Just watch me tomorrow!"

That summer, when school was out, Aisha had begun to

attend the local Qur'an course. Last summer, she had learned to sound out the words of the Qur'an. Throughout the year she had read Sura Yasin and some short suras of the Qur'an, along with her parents on Friday nights. So she had not forgotten the alphabet. Now she wanted to be able to read more fluently.

Aisha's grandma was proud of her. In spite of her age, she also wanted to learn to read the Qur'an. One day, while she was secretly trying to read the alphabet, Aisha saw her and said:

"Ohhh, grandma! I didn't know that you could read the Qur'an." Her grandmother answered:

"No, darling I always put off learning how to read it."

"You can learn it now."

"Now? But I am old, my dear, and it is very difficult to learn at my age. When you are young, it is like writing on rock, but as you get older, it is like writing on water. As people get older, they become more forgetful."

"But grandma, it is easy to learn the Qur'an. There are women in our course older than you and they are learning very quickly."

Her grandma looked at her face:

"Really? Is that true?"

"Of course it's true. Everyday our teachers remind us that Prophet Muhammad (pbuh) said that *'The most virtuous among you are the ones who learn and teach the Qur'an'*" (Bukhari, Fada'il al-Qur'an, 21).

"My sweet girl, you are right but I can't go out because of my bad legs. How can I go to the course?"

"Oh grandma, I can help you everyday when I come back home from the course."

Her grandma thought for a while and said:

"Please do not say anything about this to your parents."

"Why?"

"Because I may not be able to do it."

"I'm sure you'll be able to read. It's so easy!"

"But please don't tell them anyway. I will study in my room secretly and if I can learn, it will be a surprise for them."

With a smile, Aisha agreed. From that day on they began to study together. Even though her grandma sometimes did not have time to study, Aisha kept on teaching her patiently, because she loved her very much and she never wanted her grandma to be far away from the Qur'an.

Aisha's grandma was making slow but steady progress, learning more and more each day. At the end of two weeks, she could sound out the words of the Qur'an. She was very excited. Even she could not believe it. The old woman and Aisha decided to surprise Aisha's parents.

That night after supper, the whole family was in the living room. Aisha's father was reading the newspaper and her mother was knitting. The grandma and the granddaughter looked at each others' faces and agreed that it was the right time. Then the grandma spoke calmly, as if she were saying something completely normal:

"Do you know that Aisha and I found treasure?"

Aisha's parents looked at each other in surprise.

"Don't be so surprised! I'm telling the truth. We found treasure," continued the grandma.

They were all ears now, listening to the old woman:

"What kind of treasure?"

The grandma was glad to have gotten their attention:

"A great treasure indeed. There is everything in it, wet or dry."

Aisha's parents realized that she was trying to tell them something.

"Is it treasure, you know, with gold, silver?"

"More than that my children, there are not only a few things. There are pearls, rubies, diamonds, more than you can imagine."

Aisha joined in the conversation, her eyes shining:

"In fact, we've always had this treasure, haven't we?"

Her parents asked curiously:

"Soooo, there's treasure in our house! Where is it then?"

Aisha and her grandma smiled. The grandma nodded to the little girl. Aisha took the Qur'an and gave it to her grandma. Then the grandma opened the Qur'an, to the surprise of Aisha's parents. She began to read, first saying "Bismillahir Rahmanir Rahim" (In the name of Allah - the Merciful, the Compassionate).

Aisha's parents were in complete amazement. When she finished reading, the old woman put the Qur'an back in its cover. Aisha's father could not wait any longer and he blurted out:

"Mom, but you didn't know how to read! When did you learn?

"Aisha helped me, may Allah be pleased with her."

And she continued:

"Yes, that is the treasure we have found my dears. It is a treasure that brings Allah's good pleasure and helps us go to Heaven. The treasure of Allah's Messenger. Now tell me, can there be any other treasure greater than this?"

Aisha's parents now understood everything. And they agreed with everything that she had said. They hugged the grandma and congratulated her. Aisha watched them and she was very happy that she had helped. Remember the hadith: *"The most virtuous among you are the ones who learn and teach the Qur'an"* (Bukhari, Fada'il al-Qur'an, 21).

A BEAUTIFUL SUMMER

His bed was decorated with balloons, flags and flowers. Everyday more visitors would come, bringing him gifts. He had never had so many presents before.

That summer, Ibrahim turned nine. After the holiday had begun, Ibrahim was to be circumcised. This made Ibrahim very happy, because whatever he wanted was done in the time leading up to his circumcision. Everyone paid him a lot of attention. His bed was decorated with balloons, flags and flowers. Everyday more visitors would come, bringing him gifts. He had never had so many presents before.

Ibrahim and his family lived in Istanbul. Children who were circumcised there were brought to the Ayyub Sultan Mosque in order to visit the tomb of Ayyub Sultan. Ibrahim and his father came to Ayyub Sultan also, a week or so after he was circumcised.

First of all they came to the mosque for the afternoon prayer. There was a different atmosphere in the mosque which gave Ibrahim a feeling of wonder. Then they went up to Ayyub Sultan's tomb, opened their hands and prayed. They asked Allah to accept their payers for the sake of the blessed person who was buried in the tomb. When they finished praying, they wandered about. His father, looking at him tenderly, asked Ibrahim:

"Do you know who Ayyub Sultan was?"

"Yes Daddy. He was one of the companions of Prophet Muhammad (pbuh)."

"Yes, son, that's right. Remember the book that we read together about the life of the Prophet (pbuh). Ayyub Sultan's story is told there. When the Prophet emigrated from Makka to Madina, he stayed in Ayyub al-Ansari's house. Do you remember?"

"Yes, Daddy. Abu Ayyub is also known as Ayyub Sultan."

But Ibrahim was a bit confused:

"Daddy, how can Ayyub al-Ansari's grave be in Istanbul although he lived in Madina?"

His father smiled:

"Good question. Prophet Muhammad (pbuh) once praised the commander and soldier who would conquer Istanbul. So Abu Ayyub came to Istanbul in order to win this praise and to teach the religion of Allah to the people there."

Ibrahim:

"Ohhh, and then so many years later the Ottomans conquered Istanbul."

His father smiled. They both were very tired from walking around. They sat on a bench under the shade of the plane trees. These were huge trees. A few men could probably fit into the holes in the trees. They were probably more than a few centuries old. There were many pigeons too, which were roosting on the branches of the trees, or drinking water from the pool or preening their feathers in the water. There were also souvenir shops and many visitors. It was like a religious festival, so lively and crowded. Ibrahim looked around him curiously. Just then there was an announcement that a Qur'an recitation competition was going to begin. His father stood up:

"Let's go and listen to them...!"

They went into the mosque and sat down. There were about ten or so teenagers who had come from different cities to represent their region in the competition. When the competition began, they approached the microphone one by one and began to read suras from the Qur'an. Each one was very fluent.

Ibrahim studied the faces of his father and the other people carefully. There was a light shining from their faces. They were listening to the Qur'an with great pleasure. He also felt happier as he listened to the Qur'an. He admired these young people, who were only a few years older than him. Then the competition finished and there was a pause before the jury announced the winners. Ibrahim, taking advantage of this opportunity, asked:

"Daddy, they read really beautifully, didn't they?"

"Yes son, look, I remembered one of the hadiths of our Prophet (pbuh): *"If a group (of people) come together in one of the houses of Allah in order to read the Qur'an and to learn a lesson from it, tranquility descends upon them and Allah's Mercy covers them. And angels surround them with their wings"* (Abu Dawud, Salat, 349).

"Daddy, there are angels here, aren't there?"

"Yes, son."

"How wonderful!"

With a smile, his father said:

"Can you tell me, what kind of a book the Qur'an is?"

"It is a book revealed by Allah to the Prophet (pbuh). It was brought to him by the Archangel Gabriel."

His father went on:

"The Prophet (pbuh) read the suras and verses of the Qur'an to the people around him. They not only learned it by heart, but they wrote it down too. Do you know what the people who wrote the Qur'an were called?"

"No, Daddy."

"They were called the Scribes of the Revelation. The Prophet (pbuh) would recite the latest revelation to the people around him. The whole of the Qur'an was written down. The companions learned it by heart as well. During the Caliphate of Umar Ibn Khattab, these scriptures were compiled and during the Caliphate of Uthman Ibn Affan copies were made. In this way it has come down to our day, without a single letter being changed. It will be this way forever."

Ibrahim asked anxiously:

"You seem so sure about that. I've heard that books from other religions have been changed by people. What if the Qur'an gets changed too?"

"No, son. It is impossible, because the Qur'an is under the protection of Allah. You know if Allah does not allow it not even a leaf will move. Allah has decreed:

'Surely We have revealed the Reminder and We will most surely be its guardian.' (Maida 5:44)

Ibrahim listened to his father carefully. His father continued:

"We should live according to the Qur'an and the Sunna of Prophet Muhammad (pbuh). This is necessary to be a good Muslim."

Meanwhile the winner of the competition was going to be

announced. The competitors, their teacher and families were waiting eagerly. One of the organizers came and announced the winners. Different gifts and certificates were given to the winners. Everybody seemed very happy. Ibrahim felt envious. It was getting late. Ibrahim and his father set off for home. His father understood what Ibrahim was feeling.

"Well, son, would you like to learn to read the Qur'an?"

"Oh, yes, Daddy. I wish I could read as well as those people."

"Well, one day you will."

"Isn't it difficult?"

His father put his hand on his son's shoulder and answered:

"No, it is never difficult. Allah says: *And certainly We have made the Qur'an easy to remember, but is there anyone who will mind?*" (Qamar 54:17)

"How long will it take me to learn?"

"If you work a few hours everyday, you can learn it in a month."

Ibrahim looked up at his father's face in surprise.

"Really, so soon?"

"Sure, if you want to, I can send you to the imam of our mosque."

"That would be fantastic, Daddy."

Ibrahim liked the idea very much. He couldn't wait to tell his mother everything. It was going to be a great summer, because first he had had his circumcision, and now he was going to learn how to read the Qur'an.

THE QUR'AN IS A CURE FOR EVERY TROUBLE

The saint looked at a cloud close to the ground and he saw that there was an angel sitting on the cloud.

Zaynab was nine and her brother Fatih was ten. Their grandmother, who loved them very much, lived with them. She told them wonderful stories every evening. They loved these stories very much. The stories were so interesting that sometimes, the adults in the room listened to them too. One night, they were in the living room. The children wanted their grandmother to tell them a story. Grandma gently patted their hands:

"Well, which story should I tell you?"

Fatih said:

"How about the story of the young prince?"

Zaynab said:

"No, no! Tell us the story of the three sisters."

Grandma laughed and said:

"Hmmm, wait a minute. I've just remembered one. When I was a child, my mother told this story to me. It is the story of 'The Saint with the White Beard'. If you like, I can tell it to you."

"Oh, please grandma, please tell us."

"Alright then, sit down and listen."

The children sat and looked at their grandmother eagerly. Grandma took a deep breath and began:

"Once upon a time, long, long ago, there was a country in a distant land. The people of that country lived a quiet life. They were farmers, they sold some of their crops and kept some for themselves. One day some evil people came to this country. They taught the locals their bad habits, such as stealing and cheating. They explained to the people that in this way they would be wealthier and happier. The people there believed them. They began to steal every thing that they could. They all cheated each other and now nobody trusted anyone, they could not even sleep comfortably at night. There was no goodness left in the whole country. Finally, Allah sent them a punishment. It never rained again in that country, the rivers dried up. There was a terrible drought. The people got poorer and poorer... They could not even find any bread to eat. Everybody was worried.

In that country, a Muslim saint was living. The people went to him. Crying, they told him everything. The Muslim saint listened to them. And then he said:

"People, you were doing evil to each other and Allah has punished you."

One of them said:

"But we don't want to live like this! Our crops have dried up, our animals are ill, our children are getting thinner and thinner. Please help us!"

The saint thought for a while, stroking his white beard.

"Well," he said. "I will pray tonight. Then we will see if Allah shows us a way. But you should all repent and ask Allah's forgiveness. You must stop all your bad habits."

The people agreed. They all hugged one another and apologized for the bad deeds. Then they sincerely asked for Allah's forgiveness.

The saint with the white beard had a dream that night. In his dream, he was told to go to the country of water. He was also told this: "Don't ever forget, the Qur'an is a cure for every trouble."

The next day, the saint with the white beard set off. He passed over mountains, deserts and in the end he arrived at the country of water. It was a very interesting place. It was an island, with many flowing rivers. It always rained there and there were always clouds in the sky. The saint looked at a cloud close to the ground and he saw that there was an angel sitting on the cloud. He approached the angel and asked.

"Angel, could I speak to you please?"

"Of course," said the angel.

The saint explained the situation in his country and the plight of its people.

The angel said:

"You must be from the country whose water has been cut off. Come with me."

The old saint got on the cloud. The cloud started to rise in the air. The angel showed him a place below them:

"Look at the palace there!"

The palace that the angel showed him had hundreds of doors. A river was flowing from each door and they were destined for different places in the world. One of them was dried up and there was not even a drop of water. This river was going to the country of the old saint.

The old saint stepped down the cloud. He found that he could walk on the water easily. He walked up right in front of the palace. He found the door from which the dried up river came. It was tightly closed. The old man remembered his dream. He whispered: "The Qur'an is a cure for every trouble."

He sought refuge with Allah and began to recite verses from the Qur'an. At first the door half opened and the water began to trickle out. As he continued to recite from the Qur'an, the door opened some more. In the end, the door opened wide and water surged forward, filling the riverbed. It was crystal clear and began to flow toward the country of the old saint.

The angel who was watching from the cloud said: "Allah has accepted your and your people's prayers."

Then the angel gave him a beautiful boat. In the boat there was a magnificent treasure. The old man got in the boat and began to go back to his country on the river. In almost no time he arrived at his country.

The people who saw the roaring water along the riverbed and the boat with the old man at the wheel were very happy. They all ran toward him. The old man came out and told them everything. Then he said:

"My dear people! This water and the treasure are gifts from Allah. Don't ever abandon the Qur'an and commit such evil deeds again."

The people listened to him carefully. They shared the treasure out and they watered their gardens with the flowing water. In a short time, the land became just as it used to be, the trees bore fruit again and the animals were no longer hungry. The children began to play joyfully, the birds began to sing and the sheep to graze. All the fighting was over. These people always obeyed Allah's commandments and they began to live happily, in peace…"

"Well, children, that's the story. What do you think?"

Fatih had listened to the story carefully. His eyes were wide open:

"Grandma, is the Qur'an really a cure for every trouble?"

"Yes it is, all we need to do is to continually read it. It is the book that Allah has sent us. If we read the Qur'an and obey its rules, Allah will reward us. Look children, I will tell you a hadith: *"This Qur'an is the feast of Allah. Eat as much as you can...The beauties of Allah never end, and Allah never tires. Read, because Allah will give ten blessings for each letter of the Qur'an"* (Darimi, Fada'il al-Qur'an, 1).

Zaynab said:

"Grandma, is it true that Allah sets some rules in the Qur'an?"

Grandma said:

"Yes, my child. There is information about all kinds of things in the Qur'an, such as the names of Allah, the creation, rewards and punishments, Heaven, Hell, angels and so on... Our duties as Allah's servants and the way we should treat others are also included in the Qur'an. Besides, different kinds of worship, such as prayers, fasting, prescribed alms, pilgrimage are included there."

"They are very important for us, aren't they?"

"Of course. If we don't know these rules, how can we be good Muslims? If we read and obey the Qur'an, both this world and the other beyond it will turn into Heaven. We will please Allah."

"That sounds wonderful, grandma. Why don't we learn to read the Qur'an then?"

"Why not? If you want, I can teach you."

Zaynab said:

"Grandma, I want to learn to read the Qur'an, too."

"OK, then. From tomorrow on, I will send you to the course at the mosque. The teachers there will teach you how to read the Qur'an."

Zaynab was smiling thoughtfully:

"Zaynab, what are you smiling about?" asked Grandma.

Zaynab answered:

"What if that river floods our house too?"

They laughed cheerfully.

A LETTER FROM A FRIEND

"Allah puts the person who reads and knows the Qur'an by heart into Heaven and this person's intercession is accepted for ten people from their household who are definitely headed for Hell."

Dear Laila,

My mother says she and your mother were good friends when your parents were living here. I hope we can become good friends too. My name is Fatima. I am fifteen years old. My mother has told me that your parents want to send you to a boarding school to learn the Qur'an.

I wanted to share my feelings and experiences of when I went to the same kind of school with you. I have just come home from a boarding school, a Qur'anic boarding school, where I stayed for two years, as a student. So you can probably understand when I say that I have a lot of friends whom I love and miss very much.

One night, about three years ago my parents wanted to speak with me seriously. First of all, my father began to talk:

"Look, darling. I spoke with your mother and we wanted to ask what you thought about something that is very important for us."

I was listening to them carefully.

"You know that we are Muslims. We are trying to carry out the commands of our religion. We try to live our lives as Allah requires."

My mother looked into my eyes with compassion:

"We told you about the Qur'an, the final revelation from Allah, didn't we?"

"Sure, Mom! You taught me since I was little that we should obey the rules of the Qur'an and try to please Allah. You told me that it was necessary for being happy both in this world and in the other world."

"My darling, your father and I had a dream before you were born. We still hope that it will come true. We've been praying for this for a long time."

I was puzzled. What kind of a dream could this be? My mother looked at me with a sigh:

"Your father and I want you to be a 'hafiz' - a person who knows the whole Qur'an by heart."

I repeated in surprise:

"A person who knows the whole Qur'an by heart?"

"Yes, why not my dear? As the Prophet (pbuh) said: 'Allah puts the person who reads and knows the Qur'an by heart into Heaven and

The Path to Heaven

this person's intercession is accepted for ten people from their household who are definitely headed for Hell' (Ibn Maja, Muqaddima, 16). We want this to be true for our family."

I asked joyfully:

"Oh Mom, Dad! I would love that, but how can it be?"

My parents were pleased with my answer. They looked at each other, smiling. My father's eyes were shining. He embraced me and said:

"My darling, we are thinking of sending you to a boarding school. The religious education at this school is said to be very good. It is close to where your uncle lives. He will take care of you."

I felt very excited about the idea of going to stay in a boarding school with lots of girls of my own age. I couldn't wait to go. I jumped from my chair saying:

"Yippee!"

Even though I was happy at first, I wasn't quite so happy when I began to think about what it all meant. I realized that I would be far away from my family.

"But Mommy, how can I live far away from you?"

My mother spoke tenderly:

"I know, my darling. It won't be easy for us either. But it will be worth it, won't it?

Just think, you'll learn the Qur'an and learn how to live as a Muslim, which will make you deserve Heaven. Isn't that worth it?"

This was a very sensible answer. Yes, I would be away from my family, but in the end I would learn the book that contained Allah's commandments by heart, the book which He wants us to obey. That would be great. As a consolation, my father said :

"We can talk on the phone every week. And your uncle will be close by. I don't think you will feel lonely."

That night I went to my room very excited. I couldn't sleep until the morning. The idea of learning the Qur'an by heart made me excited, whereas the idea of staying in a strange place made me a little afraid. I had never lived away from my family before. A few weeks later, I prepared everything and left my home to go to the new school with my father. It took us a long time to get there, because it was far from my home. My uncle was waiting for us and we went to stay at his house for a few weeks before school started. I had a wonderful time playing with my cousins. Then my father had to go back home, so my uncle enrolled me at the school, which was near his house. Oh, those days! I can never forget them. I was so eager to learn the letters. It was very difficult for me, especially because I missed my family so much. I worked very hard, and I made some very good friends with the girls on the course in a very short time. They were all like angels. Everything was so wonderful! In our free time we played in the garden, we ate lots of delicious food, and we played wonderful games in the evenings. At the weekends my uncle came to take me out on little trips and to see my cousins.

In fact, I don't know how the time passed so quickly. After a few months I could read the Qur'an with the correct pronunciation. When my teacher said that I was ready to learn the Qur'an by heart, I was so happy! When I told my family this on the phone, they congratulated me and prayed for me. My dear family! How could I pay for their sacrifices? They wanted so much for me to be good and happy, both in this world and the world beyond it! The school continued for another year. With the help of my teachers and my friends, and by working very hard, Allah granted my wish and I reached my target: I memorized the whole Qur'an!

Now, I would like to tell you about the certificate ceremony. This ceremony was held in our school every year. The students were given certificates. A large crowd gathered in the hall, as it did every year. There were more than one thousand people. The relatives and the friends of the students took their seats. They were waiting for the beginning of the ceremony, for which the girls had been preparing for months. The stage was set up and the hall was decorated with balloons and flowers. In the end, the ceremony began with Qur'anic verses being recited from the loudspeakers. Our teachers read short suras from the Qur'an in their soft voices. Then our headmistress made a very moving speech. And the choir sang some hymns. Then there were some plays put on by the students, all dressed up in different costumes. Then it was our turn. The students were given their certificates. We wore specially embroidered dresses and were given Qur'ans. We took our places on stage accompanied by prayers and hymns. Our names were announced one by one and we briefly introduced ourselves. Then, while we were presented with our certificates, shiny crowns were put on our heads. I was very excited. I was so happy that I had learned the Qur'an by heart. I was also a little bit sad, because I felt lonely. All the other girls' families were there, but my family had said that they couldn't afford to come such a long distance. I was alone. Then it was my turn. My name was announced and I was called to the microphone. I thanked everybody in a trembling voice and said:

"I know that they will not hear me, but I would like to send my love to my family."

Then a voice shouted from the other side of the hall: "Fatima! My dear!" I was so surprised, it sounded just like my mother's voice. I thought that it was my imagination. Then, I heard her voice again.

"Fatima, my dear!"

I looked around the hall trying to discover where the voice was coming from. And then, I saw my mother in the crowd. I was so surprised.

"Is this really happening?" I stammered:

"M-Mommy! You're he...here!"

Running joyfully, I tried to reach my mother who was trying to get through the crowd. I was trembling because of my excitement and I was sobbing. We embraced each other. I held her so tightly. I had missed her so much. Everybody in the hall was touched and some couldn't stop themselves from crying. Many women hugged me and my mother. They were congratulating my mother. Our teachers were watching us from the stage. Our headmistress called me and my mother to the stage. Then she thanked my mother who had sent her daughter so far from her home to learn the Qur'an. I still remember her words:

"Dear sister, you have the greatest right to place the crown on your daughter's head. In a hadith, it is stated: 'Whoever reads the Qur'an and acts according to the commandments in it, Allah will dress their parents with crowns bright as sunlight and with (two) outfits unmatched in the world. Upon this, when they ask 'Why has this clothing been put on us?', they will be answered: 'Because your child reads the Qur'an.' (Darimi, Fada'il al-Qur'an, 15). Now please, here you are. This is your honor."

My lovely mother. As the headmistress spoke she became more and more excited. She put the crown on my head with trembling hands. She couldn't help crying and she thanked Allah for having let her see such a day. Then she bent down and kissed me. Yes, it was certainly the happiest day in my life. Well, that's about all. Now I am with my family at home. I am teaching the Qur'an to my brothers and some other children from the area, so that they won't have to go so far away to learn to read it. While I was away I wrote to them frequently. No matter where we are, "all Muslims are brothers and sisters." My dear friend, I saw that we are trying to obey the same rules of the same Divine Book in different parts of the world. Although there are thousands of miles between us, our hearts beat with the same love. I think there can be no stronger bond than this. I think you should thank Allah that your parents want you to also share in this honor. I am looking forward to hearing from you.

Your Friend,

Fatima

THE PICNIC

"Who wants to eat food that is more delicious than this and to go to a more beautiful place than here?"

It was a sunny day in May. The second grade was on a picnic along with their teacher and friends. Laughter and cries of joy filled the coach. The young passengers were very excited. It took one hour to reach the picnic area. They all were fascinated by the countryside around them. There were beautiful flowers everywhere; the trees were covered in blossom, birds were singing cheerfully, and butterflies were flying through the air. There was a small babbling brook near the picnic area. All the children inhaled the fresh air with pleasure. It was so good to feel the heat of the sun again, after a long winter.

They put everything out and began to play. They set up swings, the girls jumped rope and the boys had a football match. After a little while, they began to get hungry. Their teacher called:

"Come on kids! It's time to eat!"

The children had been playing energetically and now they felt very hungry. Their appetite had been sharpened by the fresh air. They opened their bags impatiently. They spread out a cloth on the ground and put their food on it. There was all sorts of food there. Fried chicken, meat balls, cakes, biscuits, fruit... They all said "Bismillahir Rahmanir Rahim" and began to eat. They ate their fill and then they put back the leftovers into their bags.

In a few minutes, they had finished. Their teacher sat on a rock and called them:

"Come on kids! Come over here!"

The students did as they were told. They looked intently at their teacher and wondered what he was going to tell them.

"So tell me! Who gave us the food we have just eaten?"

"Allah did."

"Do you love Allah?"

The Path to Heaven

Everyone said:

"Yes, we do."

"Why?"

The kids raised their hands and began to answer one by one:

"Because He created us. We would not exist if Allah had not created us."

"He made grapes, figs, apples and He also created potatoes to fry and sausages to eat so that we won't starve."

"Allah also created our families."

"Then He created trees for us to climb and flowers to smell."

"And cats to stroke."

The teacher listened to the answers with pleasure. Then, looking around, he said:

"It's very beautiful here, isn't it?"

"Yeees!"

"OK! Who wants to eat food that is more delicious than this and to go to a more beautiful place than here?"

Everybody raised their hands:

"Me, me."

The teacher smiled:

"Now guess where that beautiful place is."

"Disneyland!"

"Egypt!"

"Our town!"

"An amusement park!"

"Japan!"

The teacher answered:

"No, none of those. I know a more beautiful place than those."

The children stared at their teacher.

"Where's that?"

"The name of this beautiful place is 'Heaven' children. Heaven is a place that Allah has prepared for good people."

"Are there cakes covered in tons of chocolate?"

"What about speaking turtles and squirrels?"

"I want fancy dresses."

"Do the branches of the trees touch the sky? That would make great swings!"

The teacher answered each child by nodding his head.

"Of course there are, all these and more. When we go there Allah gives us what we want."

One of the students asked in excitement:

"What are we waiting here for? Let's go to Heaven right away!"

The teacher had not expected such an answer. He smiled and patted the student's head:

"Well, wait a minute! First of all we must deserve going to Heaven. We have to do something in this world to deserve Heaven."

"What do we need to do?"

"We must please Allah by doing good deeds."

And the teacher continued:

"Think about what we did to come on this picnic today."

The students began to answer again all at once.

"We got on the coach."

"We followed the signs on the road."

"You read the map."

Their teacher said:

"That's right. Well you need to do something to get to Heaven. And I know that you are so clever at finding the answers. Now answer these questions: Who is our guide?"

"Prophet Muhammad (pbuh)!"

"Where are the signboards that show us the way to Heaven?"

"In the Qur'an."

"And what vehicle do we use?"

"Being a good Muslim."

"Well done, my wonderful pupils!"

Satisfied with the answers, the teacher continued:

"Now, I have just remembered a hadith: *'Whoever reads the Qur'an, learns its verses by heart and takes what Allah had allowed as 'halal' (lawful) and what Allah has forbidden as 'haram' (unlawful), then Allah will put that person in heaven.'"* (Tirmidhi, Sawab al-Qur'an, 13)

One of the children said. "I know how to read the Qur'an."

"Really? When did you learn?"

"Last year. My grandma taught me."

"Excellent. How long did it take you to learn?"

"About a month."

The other children were very surprised. Some of them said, whispering among themselves: "How quickly he learned! Is it really that easy?"

Overhearing these comments, the teacher said:

"Yes, of course. It is quite easy to learn the Qur'an."

One of the students said:

"In the summer vacation I want to learn to read the Qur'an too." The others added:

"Me, too! Me too!"

Their teacher smiled:

"Why not? Of course you can. Such clever and good students can easily learn the Qur'an with the help of Allah."

It was getting late. They got back on the coach and began their return trip the same way they came. All of the students had had a good and enjoyable picnic.

THE BOY WHO SEARCHED FOR HAPPINESS

Hakan saw how happy Ali was, even with his old, beat-up bicycle. Ali did not even have a computer! Hakan wondered how Ali could be so happy.

Coming home in the evening, Mr. Ramzi parked his expensive car in the garage. He took out a brand-new mountain-bike from the trunk.

"Hakan will like this so much!" he thought to himself. Hakan had been watching him from the window. When his father called out, he went outside. Hakan did not seem very happy when he saw the new bike. After a short ride in the yard, he left the bike near the door and went back to his room. He stood before the bookcase for a while. Then he spent some time playing computer games, ignoring the books. Then he started looking out at the street from the balcony, saying "Life is so boring, everything is the same."

His parents were very worried that their son was not enjoying himself. They did everything he wanted to make him happy. All different types of entertainment were laid on for him. He always had plenty of pocket money when he went to school. He went to a private school. His teachers showed him special attention, but Hakan was just not happy. Whatever they did to make him feel better, it was no good. Last summer, they had sent him to Spain, to spend the holiday with his uncle who lived there. This had not done any good either. He was in the seventh grade. His parents knew that at his age some boys started bad habits. They felt helpless, and they were very worried about their son. Hakan did not have any friends in the neighborhood. He was really bored. Once, he decided to go for a ride in a nearby park on his bicycle. There, he met a boy of his age named Ali. After chatting for a while, they decided to have a bicycle race. Ali, who had an old bike, lost. However, he was not upset about this. The boys decided to meet at the park again the next day, and then they both went home. To Hakan's surprise, Ali seemed happy with life. The next day, when they met in the park as they had agreed, Ali did not have his bike with him, for it had broken. Instead he had a reading book. After riding for a while, Hakan lent his bike to Ali, who in return, gave his book to Hakan. Hakan began leafing through the book. A sentence on the first page caught his attention:

"Remember Me, so that I will remember you also" (2:152). In fact, this beautiful sentence was from a Qur'anic verse. The following explanation was written below:

"One cannot find true happiness by only wanting material pleasures. We must realize the presence and the greatness of our Exalted Creator and give thanks for His blessings, in everything He created for us, the food we eat being the first. The milk that we drink, for instance, comes from cows. Cows eat grass. However, it would take a great factory to turn grass into milk. We know that there is no such factory in the body of a cow. So, we know that the milk is created in the body of a cow by Allah. Thinking about such facts is the same as being with the Almighty Creator, and this gives us an inner peace." While Hakan was reading this, he began to think about the Almighty Creator. As he thought about Him some beautiful feelings began to blossom inside him. After riding for a bit, Ali came up to him. Hakan kept on reading the book. Hakan saw how happy Ali was, yet he had an old bicycle. He did not even have a computer! Hakan wondered how Ali

could be so happy.

"Can I borrow this to read?" Hakan asked. Ali said "Of course," and he added, "if you want, we can go to my house together and I will show you my books." Hakan agreed.

Ali took his new friend to his apartment. It was in an old building. When they entered the living room, Ali's mother was praying. The walls of the house were decorated with some verses from the Qur'an. He thought that the room looked like a mosque. A few minutes later Ali's mother, who had finished praying, welcomed her young guest. While Ali was showing his books to him she served them lemonade. Hakan took one of these books. While they were looking at the books, Ali's mother opened the Qur'an and began to read. This was very interesting to Hakan.

He pretended to be glancing at the book, but in reality he was studying Ali's mother and he was studying the house. The furniture in the room was old and plain. Such things did not compare with the furniture in his house. Hakan also noticed the mother's radiant face, which reflected peace and happiness. This greatly affected him. Hakan again thought about the luxurious curtains, sofas, chandeliers and silverware in his house. Ali's house was pretty simple. However, there was one thing different; the aura of peace and serenity in this house. What could be the reason for this?

Suddenly he saw a verse from the Qur'an on the wall. The translation was written under it:

"Verily in the remembrance of Allah do hearts find rest" (R'ad 13:28). Hakan learned from Ali's book that thinking of Allah means thinking about the beauties that Allah has created.

Hakan found the peace he had been looking for in Ali's home. After he looked at the books a little more, he said that he wanted to go home. Ali's mother did not want their guest to leave so quickly. She said that she could call his mother and tell her that Hakan was with them. But Hakan thanked her, and said that he really should go home, and he left on his bicycle.

When Hakan came home he began to think about the things

he had experienced that day. His mother was glad to see him looking a little bit happier. Then Hakan went up to his books. He tried to find the same beauty in these as he had in Ali's books. But unfortunately his books did not give him any peace. Hakan told his mother about his new friend. He said that he had been to their apartment. His mother was a little worried. Who were these people? The times they were living in were bad times. She thought that it might be dangerous to be friends with people you did not know. In the evening, Hakan told his father about his new friend as well. This time Hakan's mother invited Ali to their house. This new friend, who he had met only a few days earlier, had made quite a few changes in Hakan's world. Ali gave him one of his books when he visited Hakan. Hakan's mother really liked Ali too. It was obvious that he was a good boy.

The two young friends began spending more time together and Hakan became happier. One day, Hakan saw a book on Ali's table. He asked him what it was, and Ali answered:

"It is the Qur'an, Allah's revelation to Prophet Muhammad, peace be upon him. There is good advice in it which helps people to be happy. Reading it makes the heart serene. When you read the Qur'an, you think about Allah. Whoever thinks about Allah feels close to Him. This is the way to find true happiness. Also, Allah gives more spiritual rewards, what we call 'sawab', to the people who read and recite the Qur'an."

Hakan asked Ali to read the Qur'an out loud for a while. It moved Hakan very much. "I wish I could read the Qur'an." said Hakan. And Ali said that he could teach him how to read it. Then Hakan had an image of himself, learning and reading the Qur'an one day. Hakan's happiness began to grow day by day. His family was very happy about this. As the days passed, Hakan learned how to read the Qur'an and how to listen to the beautiful voices of the hafizs (people who know the Qur'an by heart) from tapes. Soon one of his favorite ways to pass his spare time became reading and listening to the Qur'an. Reading the Qur'an became one of the greatest pleasures for Hakan. He almost forgot to listen to music, especially pop music, and he listened mostly to the Qur'an.

THE BRIGHT WORLD UNDER THE EARTH

At this time, something very strange happened. Abdullah's heart began to beat again. In fact Abdullah had not died, only his heart had stopped for a little while.

In a spring morning Zaki woke up to the sound of birds singing. The branches of the plane tree in front of his house reached out toward the window of Zaki's room. Zaki generally woke up early and sat on his balcony in the clear morning air. Waking up early made him feel good.

He went to the balcony, rubbing his eyes. His parents were sitting there, reading. He greeted them:

"Assalamu alaykum, good morning Mommy, good morning Daddy." His father raised his head from the book and said:

"Wa alaykum assalam."

Zaki sat between his parents. He noticed that they were reading the Qur'an. His mother kept on reading while she patted her son's head with her free hand. At that moment Zaki remembered what his friend, Orhan, had told him yesterday.

Every night Orhan's father came home drunk. Then he would shout at his wife and children. Sometimes he even hit them. In the morning when the kids went to school, he would be asleep. He woke up in the afternoon, and then late at night he would come back home, drunk again. Not one day would go by when that drunk left his family alone. While Zaki was thinking about this, his father finished reading and began to pray. As he was praying, Zaki sat on his father's lap and said "Amen." A few minutes later, his mother also finished reading and went to prepare the breakfast. Zaki asked his father why Orhan's father was always drunk and why he hit his children. His father said:

"Well, son, Allah forbade the drinking of alcohol in the Qur'an. It is a very bad habit. Maybe Orhan's father does not know this. Or maybe he can't help drinking."

"Let's pray for him to stop drinking daddy."

"That's a good idea, son, but we can pray not only to stop drinking, but to stop all kinds of bad habits. We should pray for all Muslims."

Meanwhile, his mother had got breakfast ready. They were happy while they ate their breakfast. The sunlight came in from the balcony, lighting up the room. Zaki did not have school that day. While his father was leaving home for work, Zaki and his mother prayed for his well-being.

Zaki never wasted his time. When he did not have any homework, he always found something to do. Either he helped his mother or he read a book. Today, he was going to read again. The day before, his father had given him a new story book. While he was leafing through it, the name of a story caught his attention. "The Bright World Under the Earth." Zaki began to read this story:

There was a great scholar, called Abdullah, who served Islam with the books he wrote. This scholar spent his days studying. One night, he became ill while writing a book called 'The Lights of the Qur'an.' In a few minutes, he fell asleep. When it was the time for morning prayer, his son wanted to wake him up:

"Daddy! Get up! It's prayer time!" he said. But his father didn't respond. The boy tried a few times more. But unfortunately, his father was not even breathing. Then the boy's mother came. She looked at her husband carefully. The man was completely still.

Suddenly, she started to scream. She called the neighbors. "Oh!" they said, "He's dead!" Then they called the imam. The father was taken to the mosque. After the body had been cleansed, the funeral prayer was performed. Then the man was buried in the graveyard. The family was very sad. At this time, something very strange happened. Abdullah's heart began to beat again. In fact Abdullah had not died, only his heart had stopped for a little while. Everybody had thought that he was dead. Luckily, when he was buried there remained a hole in the earth above him, and he could breathe from that hole. Abdullah was in a dark and narrow place. He did not understand what had happened, and he was very frightened. He thought that there had been an earthquake and that now he was buried under the debris. He began to shout so that he would be heard:

"Help! Rescue me!" No one answered. He shouted again:

"Help! Heeelp!"

Just then, he heard another voice.

"Don't shout! Nobody can hear you. It is night time now. They will only be able to hear you in the morning."

Abdullah was surprised. Who was speaking? He was not scared, he was even glad that there was somebody who could hear him.

"Who are you?" asked Abdullah.

"I am the one lying in this grave." answered the voice.

"Well, how do you know that it is night now?"

"Look at the light in my grave. The light in my grave is different in the morning and at night."

"How is that possible?" asked Abdullah.

"All my life I read the suras of Mulk at night and Yasin during the day. After I died Allah created lights from these suras. These lights light up my grave both day and night."

After this conversation, Abdullah understood that he had no choice other than to wait for morning. When morning came, he shouted again:

"Help me! Rescue me!"

Some people passing by heard him and rescued him from the grave. His wife, children and his neighbors were all very happy that he was alright.

Abdullah, who was also known by the name Qadi Baydawi, continued reading and he wrote many more books. The books he read filled libraries. "Anwar al-Tanzeel," his interpretation of the Qur'an, which means "The Lights of the Qur'an" has been read by millions of Muslims throughout the centuries.

Zaki really enjoyed reading this story. It was a true story. He told the sory to his mother. "Yes my darling, Qadi Baydawi was a famous scholar. He wrote an interpretation of the Qur'an." she said.

Zaki was impressed by the story. He heard from his parents that they read the suras of Yasin and Mulk everyday. He said to himself:

"Mom and Dad are so clever! Their graves will be luminous too."

When his father came home in the evening, Zaki told him about the story he had read and he said that he wanted to learn how to read the Qur'an as soon as possible. The father patted his son on the back and said:

"I'm proud of you son. You are a good boy. I will teach you how to read the Qur'an very quickly."

SWEET GRANDPA

"He who reads the Qur'an does not become senile when he is old nor does he lose his strength."

Ahmad's grandfather was a cheerful, soft spoken, honest man. He had white beard and all the children called him "Sweet Grandpa" and the adults called "Grandpa Ghazi" (war veteran). Everybody in the neighborhood loved him. He was very old, nearly ninety. He was still able to walk around slowly. He liked chatting with people and he spent most of his time reading the Qur'an. While walking, with the aid of his cane, to the mosque he would greet all the children he saw. He gave candy to the children that gathered around him after prayer time, and he stroked their heads.

Sweet Grandpa was a war veteran. He had fought in Gallipoli. He told the children many things about the heroic soldiers in Gallipoli. One evening, Sweet Grandpa was telling them about his memories.

Ahmad asked: "Grandpa, what does ghazi mean?"

"My dear, if a soldier fighting against an enemy die at war, then he is called a martyr, the ones who survive the war - sometimes they are wounded - are called ghazis."

Ahmad asked:

"Grandpa, how old were you when you went off to war?"

When he heard this question, tears welled up in Grandpa's eyes, then he began to tell about the day he joined up:

"It was a beautiful spring day. I was just eighteen years old. It was my wedding day. Drums were beating in the square and the wedding meal was being cooked in the pots. There were horse races and a wrestling competition. Everybody was dancing happily. At that time, three soldiers came to the village. They were exhausted. We immediately gave them some food. While they were eating they called the headman of the village. The headman's face changed suddenly.

Then he made an announcement to the people:

"Dear villagers! Please be quiet and listen to me. These soldiers have some news from the government. All the young men in the village should gather in the village square in two hours' time. They will go to Gallipoli with these soldiers."

For a while, there was no sound from the crowd. There was a deep silence. The silence was broken by Mehmed, who was the winner of the wrestling competition that had taken place a few minutes earlier:

"For the sake of Allah, the Qur'an and our country, we sacrifice our lives! Allahu akbar, Allahu akbar! (Allah is the greatest)" he shouted. The other young men began to repeat his words:

"For the sake of Allah, the Qur'an and our country, we sacrifice our lives! Allahu akbar, Allahu akbar!"

The drums began to beat again, but this time it was for both the wedding and the soldiers. I had to go to war too. I was going off to war on my wedding day. While I was thinking about your grandmother, a child came up to me and gave me a note. It was from her:

"My dear Ali, for Allah, the Qur'an and our country, you should go to war, too. Don't worry about me!"

When I read this letter from my fiancée, I felt better. Your grandma was our neighbor's daughter. We learned the Qur'an together when we were children. She used to tell me about her grandfather. Before he was martyred in Galicia, he had written to her and her brothers and sisters:

"If we do not fight here, the enemies will invade our country and take the Qur'an away from us."

All the young men of the village took their leave and went to Gallipoli. Then the war began. In "Anafartalar," we bravely defended our country for days against the enemy. The war was fierce but we soldiers managed to remain calm, even cheerful. We knew that the ones who died protecting our country would be martyrs and go to Heaven. This was a power taken from the Qur'an, something which we never abandoned. We prayed and read the Qur'an as much as possible. The soldiers who didn't know how to read the Qur'an said:

"I wish I could read it, then I would gain more blessings."

They recited the short suras of the Qur'an, which they knew by heart and prayed. One day a lot of our friends were martyred, yet they all became birds of Heaven. The enemies learned a good lesson.

Some of us were able to go back to our villages, by the grace of Allah. We had a new wedding and I married your grandmother."

The children were listening to their Grandpa intently. Their mother brought them some fruit. The children were tired and sleepy.

But Ahmad asked eagerly:

"Grandpa, you always tell us about your life and the books you have read. But Moustapha, our neighbor's son told me that his grandfather is younger than you, but he cannot remember much about when he was younger. He cannot tell us about anything he did, not like you."

His grandfather answered:

"My son, the source of my health and happiness is the Qur'an. Our Prophet stated that *'He who reads the Qur'an does not become senile when he is old nor does he lose his strength'*" (Hakim, at-Targhib wa't-Tarhib, 3, 278)

Grandpa then said that that was enough for the evening and that he was tired. He was going to go to his room to read the Qur'an and then sleep. He would get up early in the morning and read the Qur'an before morning prayer. He never forgot to do this. Their grandmother also used to read the Qur'an now and then. Grandpa had mentioned this a few times and once he said:

"My dears, reading the Qur'an early in the morning brings you peace. And our Prophet states: *'If the Qur'an is read in a house it becomes a very peaceful place. Angels are present in that house, devils are driven away and abundance and goodness increase there. As for the house in which the Qur'an is never read; in contrast, it turns into a place of unrest, where no angels, but only devils are present, abundance and goodness decrease'*" (Haythami, Majma' al-Zawa'id, 7/171).

Time had passed quickly, listening to Sweet Grandpa. Now it was time for the children to go to bed. The next morning at breakfast the children made a decision. They would read the Qur'an like their Grandpa and parents. There were only two weeks left before the summer holiday started. As soon as the schools closed they would go to the mosque to learn the Qur'an and they would study hard.